TOTAL LIFE STEWARDSHIP

5 STAGES OF SUCCESS

> KNOW YOUR DESIGN
> MAXIMIZE YOUR TALENTS
> MANAGE YOUR MONEY
> TEACH YOUR CHILDREN
> FINISH WELL

ISBN: 978-156427-337-6

Cover Design: Dwayne Bassett

Printed in the U.S.A.

The study is recorded from a live event.

Special thanks to

Handre deJongh, Bob Dickie, Chuck Bentley, Catherine Brown, David McAlvany, AJ Parker, Jim Armstrong, Dwayne Bassett, Susan Ellington, Heather Stanfield, Arielle Vogel, Sheila Thompson, Hannah Simic, and Katie Logan for your help putting together this study.

Our Prayer

Our prayer is that God will use this study to bless you in this life and more importantly, for the day you stand before the Lord.

1 Corinthians 4:2

YOUR PRESENTERS

Handre deJongh

Handre deJongh became involved with Crown Financial Ministries as a Career Direct® counselor in 2002 and joined Crown full-time in July 2005. Handre's passion for building potential in individuals and teams is evident in the more than 1,300 individuals and numerous teams he has helped find purpose and alignment in life, studies and operations. In July 2012, Handre joined the Crown Home Office team in a Director role, overseeing the US field team, serving as the International liaison between Crown Home Office and the Ministry Expansion Officers and was recently promoted to the role of Vice President of Global Outreach in 2017. Handre has been married to Marelise since 1996 and they have three children. They reside in Knoxville, Tennessee.

Bob Dickie

Prior to serving as President of Crown Financial Ministries, Bob was a Captain in the United States Air Force with extensive duty in Europe and Asia. He is also a former CEO for an international training and sales materials service provider that he helped triple in size over four years. His work has spanned several industries and included both high growth and turnaround environments for multiple companies. He and his wife, Brandi, both graduates of the University of Tennessee, live in Knoxville, Tennessee with their six children and two dogs. Bob is an avid outdoor lover, mountain climber, and competitive runner.

Chuck Bentley

As our CEO, Chuck Bentley has a relentless passion to travel the globe teaching biblical financial principles to stewards from all walks of life including the affluent, middle class, poor, and ultra poor. In addition, Chuck writes and produces a daily radio broadcast heard on over 1,200 outlets in the USA. Chuck and his wife, Ann, both graduates of Baylor University, have been married since 1978. They can be found reading and spending time outdoors with their family at their home in Knoxville, Tennessee when they are not traveling the world together to advance Crown's mission. They have four adult sons, a daughter-in-law, and four grandchildren.

Catherine Brown

Catherine has served with Crown since 2009. Her desire to spread the message of biblical Stewardship reaches into all areas: churches, businesses, organizations and outreach/rehab centers. Catherine is one of Crown's most active Career Direct Consultants and teaches unapologetically that "we are best when we are following the design God has for our lives...not one that we construct on our own." Her current passion is teaching young adults who are transitioning into financial independence, and she is in the midst of creating a curriculum supporting this topic. Catherine lives with her husband, Paul, and two college-aged children in Birmingham, Alabama.

David McAlvany

David is CEO of the McAlvany Financial Companies--International Collectors Associates (a 45-year-old precious metals brokerage firm), ICA Europe, and McAlvany Wealth Management. He is a featured speaker on national television programs (including CNBC, Fox News, Fox Business News, and Bloomberg), on radio programs, and at financial seminars around the world. He can be heard weekly on his market commentary with world leaders, bankers, economists, and renowned investors at www.mcalvany.com. David is a graduate of Biola University and is an associate member of Keble College, Oxford University, where he studied philosophy and political theory. His interests are varied, but he has a keen passion for cycling and mountaineering. He spends his free time with his wife and their children skiing, hiking, and enjoying the mountains of Colorado.

INTRODUCTION

Total. Life. Stewardship.

An Introduction by Chuck Bentley

What is it? What does it look like?

Maybe these three words bring a specific person to mind—someone you would say is a great example. Or maybe you don't have a vision for what it looks like at all.

Total Life Stewardship is a high calling from our Heavenly Father; an invitation to not just manage resources well, but to become a steward, live as a steward and prepare for the day when your stewardship will be evaluated.

The 5 Stages of Success exist to help you think through and answer certain questions about your life with intention: Who am I? Why am I here? What is my purpose? What is God's plan for the resources He has entrusted to me? What is His plan for the people around me? What is my role in their lives? What does God want the end result of my life to be?

In the chapters ahead, we will help you Know Your Design, Maximize Your Talent, Manage Your Money, Teach Your Children, and Finish Well. We also have included a special testimony of an outstanding example. The content is both practical and spiritual. Not only will you find help for your present challenges, but knowledge to prepare you for "that day" when we each stand before the Lord Jesus. We pray that these lessons will inspire you to live with the ultimate goal in mind, to hear Jesus say, "Well done, thy good and faithful servant! Enter into the joy of your Master."

Instructions:

This study is designed for you to be able to do on your own, with a spouse or friend, as a family, or even in a church small group. Pray for and allow God to show you how He wants to use it in your life and in the lives of people around you.

When you are ready to begin, start by watching the first video—Stage 1. In this workbook, there is a listening guide that accompanies each stage. As you watch the video, fill in the blanks and use the additional space to take notes.

The videos for each stage are about 45-50 minutes each with a "pause" in each session. You can use the pause to divide it into 2 shorter sessions, or you can simply use the pause to think through or discuss what stood out to you most from part 1 before moving on to part 2. If you choose not to pause at all, the video will continue after 10 seconds.

Once you've finished watching a message, answer the questions for individual reflection or group discussion in your workbook. If you are using this as a small group study, your group may want to answer the questions immediately after watching the video, or, you may want to have group members briefly highlight immediate takeaways, close in prayer, and give everyone personal time over the next week to answer the questions and return for group discussion the following week. Also remember to commit that week's verse to memory over the next week.

Following the reflection and discussion questions is a section that can be used like a journal. This section should help you apply God's principles from each stage to your own life. What are the next steps He's asking you to take? What has He put on your heart and how can you set goals to help you intentionally pursue His path?

Conclusion:

The 5 Stages of Success will help you not only with practical problems of today but will assist you to serve God's purposes and become a success in His eyes as you pursue the eternal reward of pleasing Him.

Remember: the biggest financial mistake you could make is *not* getting too far into debt, writing checks that bounce, overdrawing your account or buying a lottery ticket. The worst financial mistake you could make would be to become a success in the eyes of the world, but a failure when it comes to aligning your life to what God says about money.

Commit to spend the next several weeks focusing on ordering your life in such a way that God can spend you however He wants. By the end of the study, my hope is that you can say, "God, you came to fix my heart and to give me an eternal destiny, an eternal identity, and an eternal job to serve you with all my heart and soul. Help me to use money as your steward to do good on this earth. Help me to use all you've entrusted to me to bring your goodness to the world, to bless my family, to take care of my needs, to give to my church. Help me use all my resources—my identity, talent, money, relationships, and time—to grow your Kingdom."

STAGE ONE

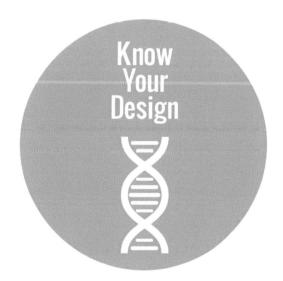

KNOW YOUR DESIGN

(Presenter: Handre deJongh)

MEMORY VERSE

"For you created my inmost being; you knit me together in my mother's womb. I praise you because I am fearfully and wonderfully made; your works are wonderful, I know that full well."

Psalm 139:13-14 (NIV)

LISTENING GUIDE – PART 1

Fill in the blanks as you watch the video.

Like everyone, the people Handre observed in Hong Kong were searching for _____ , _____ , and _____ , just in the wrong place.

The two most asked questions in the world today are:

Who am I? (What is my _____ ?)

Why am I here? (What is my _____ ?)

In the coffee taste test, Pastor Ryan found his coffee to be

_____ . Pastor Ronnie found the coffee to be

_____ . Mike observed that his coffee exuded

notes of Swiss _____ , citrus and hazelnuts.

"Life is like a cup of coffee, it all depends on how it is

_____ ."

- "Bitter coffee" can describe a job I do not like but cannot

  get out of because of _____ . I am

  desperately looking forward to _____ .

- "Weak coffee" describes a job that is way below my

  _____ .

- "Perfect coffee" describes a job in which I am

  experiencing _____ on a daily basis.

Statistics show that _____ % of people are not satisfied

in their jobs.

It is extremely important for us to _____

that where we spend 60% of our time that we are awake is

important with regards to the rest of our _____ .

LISTENING GUIDE – PART 2

Fill in the blanks as you watch the video.

Four Major Areas That Comprise Your Unique Design:

1. Personality

Over an 80-year lifespan, we can change our personality only _____ %. Personality is unique to you as an _____ . It is from the _____ out, not the _____ in.

"Before I formed you in the _____ I knew you;
Before you were born I _____ you;
I _____ you a prophet to the nations."
Jeremiah 1:5 (NKJV)

_____ is from the outside in. It can _____ as we are exposed to different environments (filters).

Who I am is _____ . How I act and behave is a result of my _____ .

2. Interests

Based on your character and environment, your

interests can change. You must have the help of

_____ to determine which interests you

should pursue.

3. Skills

Learned skills take a lot of _____ .

_____ skills require minimum effort.

4. Values

Values are the _____ (values base) that we

have adopted. They must _____ with the other

three areas.

When all 4 areas line up, you have a _____

cup of coffee. If you know your _____ , you

will know your _____ .

Jesus knew His purpose:

"Then Pilate said to him, 'So you are a king?' Jesus answered, 'You say that I am a king. For this _____ I was born and for this purpose I have come into the world—to bear witness to the _____. Everyone who is of the truth listens to my voice.'"

John 18:37 (ESV)

DISCUSSION QUESTIONS

Be prepared to discuss your responses within your group.

1. As in the example of Hong Kong's busy fortune tellers, people today are going to great lengths, and often in the wrong places, to discover who they are and why they are here. How about you—what things or individuals might be competing with God as your source for identity and purpose?

2. Think about your own personality. How has your personality been consistent through the years?

3. How would you describe your own personality? King David acknowledged that he was *"fearfully and wonderfully made"* (Psalm 139:14). Could you say the same about yourself? Why or why not?

4. The Job Satisfaction graph ranges from 1 to 10. Where would you rank your own job satisfaction?

   Based on your ranking, would you say your "coffee" is...Bitter? Weak? Perfect?

   Specify any pressing obligations or unused talents that may be causing frustration with your job.

5. People's relationships can be affected either positively or negatively by the degree to which they experience job fulfillment. Do you sometimes experience friction with family or friends that can be traced back to a deficiency in job satisfaction—either yours or theirs? Give an example.

6. If you are experiencing a lack of passion in your career, which of the four areas (personality, interests, skills, values) may be misaligned?

7. Paul reminded Timothy that God saved and called us *"because of his own purpose and grace"* (2 Timothy 1:9 NIV). In other words, God has a plan in mind regarding each of His children. How does knowing your identity and purpose relate to your successful stewardship of God's gifts and blessings?

NEXT STEPS AND GOALS

As you reflect on the video and discussion questions from Stage One, what are the next steps God is asking you to take to understand more about your unique God-given personality and how He wants to use you?

If you are interested in learning more about your personality, be sure to visit crown.org/pid to learn more about Crown's *Personality I.D.*® assessment.

STAGE TWO

MAXIMIZE YOUR TALENTS

(Presenter: Bob Dickie)

MEMORY VERSE

"For I know the plans I have for you," declares the Lord, "plans to prosper you and not to harm you, plans to give you hope and a future. Then you will call on me and come and pray to me, and I will listen to you. You will seek me and find me when you seek me with all your heart. I will be found by you," declares the Lord, "and will bring you back from captivity. I will gather you from all the nations and places where I have banished you," declares the Lord, "and will bring you back to the place from which I carried you into exile."

Jeremiah 29:11-14 (NIV)

LISTENING GUIDE – PART 1

Fill in the blanks as you watch the video.

Momentous events, like the assassination of JFK and the 9/11 attacks, become indelibly imprinted in our memories. Another more recent event, known as the "Great _____," occurred in 2008 and 2009, with worldwide ramifications.

There's no doubt that economic rules are changing. They are being fundamentally rewritten, leading to a _____ shift.

Something else that is changing is the way that we minister. Not only do we give a person a cup of cold _____ , meeting their needs and pain points, but we also bring them along with us in a _____ .

The world is always looking for new ways to overcome challenges, but God wants us to go back to the fundamental truths in _____ . There we understand that God has a design for how we can have _____ .

Many prognosticators are saying that the 2008-2009 economic _____ was just an anomaly and that plans are in place to prevent it from happening again. However, indications are that it will be bigger and worse.

But, it is during those times that we have the opportunity to

_____ people. We need to be prepared to

give them _____ counsel.

The Data Explosion:

Today, we have a data explosion that is the

_____ for the new economy. Data fuels

Artificial Intelligence, the economic engine. This engine

drives such things as Virtual Reality, Automation and

_____ Reality.

This is impacting every sector in our society, including:

Data Storage

- People are searching for ways to store data, even

  utilizing human _____ .

Education

We have an education "_____" that is about

to burst.

- Student loan costs are going through the roof.

- Online _____ is causing universities to revamp their curriculums.

- Change is required in order for institutions to remain _____ .

Law

- Fewer lawyers are needed to argue cases due to _____ .

- Fees are rising because there are still things like experience, strategy, creativity and _____ that automation cannot do.

Healthcare

- Machines can now read MRIs faster and more accurately than _____ .

Auto & Transportation

- Worldwide this is a _____ dollar a year industry.

- 15% of the U.S. male population has a job that is tied to _____ .

STAGE TWO

Notes

- Many stand to lose their jobs due to automation, such as _____ cars.

Retail

- This sector is being harmed by _____ .

We need to help our children engineer their lives differently than their parents and grandparents did. Otherwise, we're setting them up for _____ .

Students must learn to live within their God-given _____ . For those who have not, the average time it takes to graduate from college is now approaching _____ .

LISTENING GUIDE – PART 2

Fill in the blanks as you watch the video.

So how can we teach our children and others in our community to maximize their talent?

1. _____ from every experience. We can

   learn from _____ .

2. Seek and learn from _____ .

3. Never stop learning. Always be in a learning

   _____ .

4. Use your _____ . Help people

   _____ their skill sets.

5. Don't be _____ . We need to help others

   develop a strong work _____ .

6. Seek the right environment to _____ .
   The wrong crowd can move you in the wrong

   _____ .

7. Do all things for the _____ of God. We
   need to learn to walk in _____ and trust
   God.

In spite of all the changes and challenges before

us, we must always remember: "God has got our

_____ ."

DISCUSSION QUESTIONS

Be prepared to discuss your responses within your group.

1. Abraham experienced a "tectonic change" in his life when God called him to leave his home country (see Hebrews 11:8). Share an example from your own experience where an unexpected event required you to make significant changes.

2. Would you say that you are better prepared to help others as a result? How?

3. If you have a higher education degree, are you currently working in that field? If you could go back to school, would you change your major? Why or why not?

4. Proverbs 13:20 says, *"Walk with the wise and become wise; associate with fools and get in trouble"* (NLT). Name some ways you can help foster the right environment in which your children can grow and succeed.

5. Paul reminds us, *"...Whatever you do, do all to the glory of God!"* (1 Corinthians 10:31 ESV). How does working within your God-given design bring glory to Him?

6. Share any changes you need to make in order to truly maximize your talents.

7. In view of today's "data explosion," what advice would you give to your children or others as they make plans for training and/or higher education?

8. God promises that He's "got our back" (see Deuteronomy 31:6). How does that assurance help with the changes and challenges of life?

9. Tell of an instance when that truth became real in your life.

STAGE TWO

NEXT STEPS AND GOALS

As you reflect on the video and discussion questions from Stage Two, what are the next steps God is asking you to take to better understand the gifts and talents He's equipped you with and how He wants to maximize your talent for His glory.

After prayerful consideration of Stage Two: Maximize Your Talent, if you believe God is leading you to make a career change, you may want to take our free assessment at http://pivot.crown.org.

STAGE THREE

MANAGE YOUR MONEY

(Presenter: Chuck Bentley)

MEMORY VERSE

"Everything in the heavens and earth is yours, O Lord, and this is your kingdom. We adore you as being in control of everything. Riches and honor come from you alone, and you are the ruler of all mankind; your hand controls power and might, and it is at your discretion that men are made great and given strength. O our God, we thank you and praise your glorious name."

1 Chronicles 29:11-13 (TLB)

Note: Before watching this session, you may want to watch the following video clip, which Chuck references at the beginning of his message: http://bit.ly/TotalLifeStewardship3

This particular segment is used for illustration purposes only and does not constitute Crown's endorsement of the film.

LISTENING GUIDE – PART 1

Fill in the blanks as you watch the video.

Only 10 years ago _____ % of working Americans were living paycheck to paycheck. Today, _____ % say they are living month to month just to get by.

We have a serious _____ of financial problems, but we also have an epidemic of bad financial _____ that doesn't align with

_____ _____ .

Even though a person has been raised in church, they can still be biblically _____ about what God says about money. God gave us His _____ for our own good.

Stewardship is *not* managing money in such a way that you can spend whatever you want. True biblical _____ is managing your money in such a way that God can spend _____ however He wants.

In Matthew 6, Jesus says that we are to _____ in secret, _____ in secret and _____ in secret. Why? So that we will see that He is real.

In Matthew 6:19-21, Jesus tells us: *"Do not lay up for yourselves treasures on earth, where moth and rust destroy and where thieves break in and steal, but lay up for yourselves treasures in heaven, where neither moth nor rust destroys and where thieves do not break in and steal. For where your treasure is, there your heart will be also"* (ESV).

Where you put your _____ is an indication of what you really _____ .

God wants us to learn to put our treasure in His _____.

Money is an _____ of who you are really serving.

In Matthew 6:31-33, Jesus says, *"Therefore do not be anxious, saying, 'What shall we eat?' or 'What shall we drink?' or 'What shall we wear?' For the Gentiles seek after all these things, and your heavenly Father knows that you need them all. But seek first the kingdom of God and his righteousness, and all these things will be added to you"* (ESV).

God says that He wants to take care of us, and in exchange, He wants us to make Him first on the _____ of our heart.

A deception of Satan is belief that money is our _____, that money will provide us everything we need. But God says, no, we've got that wrong—we have it _____ _____ .

What's wrong with the way we allocate money? It starts with the question: Who's your _____ ? (Psalm 24:1)

The first step in understanding _____ is that we don't own everything—God does.

STAGE THREE

Notes

LISTENING GUIDE – PART 2

Fill in the blanks as you watch the video.

Honor God with the _____ of all your income. Giving to _____ must come first.

Instead of thinking about a "giving" bucket, we should think about it as _____ in heaven.

Statistics say 10% of Christians give 10%, and 30% of Christians give _____ .

Larry Burkett said that there is enough money in the hands of Christians to fund the _____ _____ all over the world, but Christians don't let go of it.

God is always faithful, and the successful _____ is one who is faithful in return.

Credit cards have become the emergency _____ account of our culture.

The U.S. has the lowest _____

_____ of any developed nation on planet Earth.

It's great to be debt free. But it is a _____

to think that being debt free is the goal of the Christian life.

Today we spend _____ % of everything we get on

ourselves.

This is God's way:

1. He is our _____ .

2. We are to lay up _____ in heaven.

3. We are to have the wisdom to _____ .

When we do these three things first, God takes care of all

the rest. Seek first His _____, and He'll take

care of your "_____ ."

When we get to heaven, we will be stewarding what

_____ to Him.

The meek will inherit the earth, because their

_____ has been changed.

DISCUSSION QUESTIONS

Be prepared to discuss your responses within your group.

1. If the Bible is full of financial wisdom, how it is that many Christians are ignorant about what God's Word says about money?

2. What are some of the sources many people rely on for financial advice?

3. It's easy to fall into the trap of viewing money as a source of security. What is faulty about this view?

4. Proverbs 3:9 tells us, *"Honor the Lord with your wealth and with the firstfruits of all your produce"* (ESV). What happens in our hearts when we choose to give to God first?

What reasons might we give for not doing this?

5. Jesus observed the widow giving her two mites, all that she had (see Mark 12:42-44). Why do you think Jesus drew the disciples' attention to her act?

6. Is it time to reevaluate your financial priorities?

7. We are given the example of the ant in Proverbs 6:6-8. Why are its actions considered wise?

Would you say that you are a wise saver? Why or why not?

8. True stewardship begins with a changed heart. How has your heart been changed?

9. Has God been giving you opportunities to trust Him more fully? What has been your response?

10. In the parable of the talents (see Matthew 25:14-30), the two faithful stewards were commended by their Master. What are some of the things that God has entrusted to you as a steward?

Which are you faithfully putting to use?

Which need more attention?

NEXT STEPS AND GOALS

As you reflect on the video and discussion questions from Stage Three, what are the next steps God is asking you to take to be a better steward of the material resources He has entrusted to you?

To learn how your beliefs and behaviors about money align with God's Word, visit crown.org/mli to take Crown's free MoneyLife® Indicator Assessment.

FORMS/WORKSHEETS

If you do not have a consistent plan for tracking your spending and sticking with a budget, you may find the worksheets on the following pages helpful.

For additional practical tips and helpful resources, visit crown.org, select "Resources," then under the Personal Finance options click on "Budgeting." Finally, choose and download *The Easy Guide to a Budget You'll Love*.

Included on the following pages are:

1. **Spending Guidelines for:**

    a. A single person without a roommate

    b. A family of four

    (For additional spending guidelines that better fit your stage of life, select "Spending Guidelines" on page 10 of *The Easy Guide to a Budget You'll Love*.)

2. **A Spending Tracker**

3. **An Estimated Budget Worksheet**

Suggested Percentage Guidelines for Family Income

Single with No Children/ Living Alone

Gross Household Income	$25,000	$35,000	$45,000	$55,000	$85,000	$125,000
Tithe/Giving	10.0%	10.0%	10.0%	10.0%	10.0%	10.0%
Taxes						
1. Federal*	6.98%	9.27%	10.54%	12.67%	17.02%	20.15%
2. Social Security**	6.20%	6.20%	6.20%	6.20%	6.20%	6.20%
3. Medicare**	1.45%	1.45%	1.45%	1.45%	1.45%	1.45%
4. State*	0.00%	2.00%	2.00%	2.00%	2.00%	2.00%
5. Other*	0.00%	0.00%	0.00%	0.00%	0.00%	0.00%
Total Taxes***	16.63%	18.92%	20.19%	22.32%	26.67%	29.80%
Net Spendable Income:	$18,344	$24,879	$31,414	$37,224	$53,829	$75,250
3. **Housing**	40%	38%	36%	34%	32%	30%
4. **Food**	6%	6%	7%	7%	7%	7%
5. **Transportation**	15%	15%	14%	14%	13%	13%
6. **Insurance**	4%	4%	4%	5%	5%	5%
7. **Debts**	5%	5%	5%	5%	5%	5%
8. **Entertainment / Rec**	6%	6%	7%	7%	8%	8%
9. **Clothing**	5%	6%	6%	7%	8%	8%
10. **Savings**	5%	5%	5%	5%	5%	5%
11. **Health/Wellness**	6%	5%	5%	5%	4%	4%
12. **Miscellaneous**	5%	6%	6%	6%	7%	7%
13. **Investments****	3%	4%	5%	5%	6%	7%

All your net spendable income percentages should add up to 100%

If you have school/childcare expenses, these percentages must be deducted from other categories

14. **Education****	3%	7%	8%	9%	10%	10%

*The most accurate way to determine your Federal, State, and Other tax withholdings is to check your last Federal and State tax returns. The numbers on the chart above are only estimates using 2015 tax rates, $4,000 exemption/person, and standard.

**If you are an employee, this is the correct amount withheld from your paychecks. If you are self-employed, the amounts double to 12.4% for Social Security and 2.90% for Medicare.

***In some cases earned income credit (EIC) will apply. It may be possible to increase the number of deductions to lessen the amount of tax paid per month. Review the last tax return for specific information.

****This category is used for long-term investment planning, such as college education or retirement.

*****This category is added as a guide only. If you have this expense, the percentage shown must be deducted from other budget.

CROWN
Do Well

crown.org

Suggested Percentage Guidelines for Family Income

Married with 2 Children

Gross Household Income	$25,000	$35,000	$45,000	$55,000	$85,000	$125,000
Tithe/Giving	10.0%	10.0%	10.0%	10.0%	10.0%	10.0%
Taxes						
1. Federal*	0.00%	1.83%	3.64%	5.52%	8.87%	12.55%
2. Social Security**	6.20%	6.20%	6.20%	6.20%	6.20%	6.20%
3. Medicare**	1.45%	1.45%	1.45%	1.45%	1.45%	1.45%
4. State*	0.00%	2.00%	2.00%	2.00%	2.00%	2.00%
5. Other*	0.00%	0.00%	0.00%	0.00%	0.00%	0.00%
Total Taxes*	7.65%	11.48%	13.29%	15.17%	18.52%	22.20%
Net Spendable Income:	$20,588	$27,483	$34,518	$41,155	$60,760	$84,751
3. **Housing**	39%	36%	32%	30%	30%	29%
4. **Food**	15%	12%	13%	12%	11%	11%
5. **Transportation**	15%	12%	13%	14%	13%	13%
6. **Insurance**	5%	5%	5%	5%	5%	5%
7. **Debts**	5%	5%	5%	5%	5%	5%
8. **Entertainment / Rec**	3%	5%	4%	7%	7%	8%
9. **Clothing**	4%	5%	6%	6%	7%	7%
10. **Savings**	5%	5%	5%	5%	5%	5%
11. **Health/Wellness**	5%	6%	6%	5%	5%	5%
12. **Miscellaneous**	4%	4%	6%	6%	7%	7%
13. **Investments****	0%	5%	5%	5%	5%	5%

All your net spendable income percentages should add up to 100%

If you have school/childcare expenses, these percentages must be deducted from other categories

| 14. **School/Childcare***** | 8% | 6% | 5% | 5% | 5% | 5% |

*The most accurate way to determine your Federal, State, and Other tax withholdings is to check your last Federal and State tax returns. The numbers on the chart above are only estimates using 2015 tax rates, $4,000 exemption/person, and standard.

**If you are an employee, this is the correct amount withheld from your paychecks. If you are self-employed, the amounts double to 12.4% for Social Security and 2.90% for Medicare.

***In some cases earned income credit (EIC) will apply. It may be possible to increase the number of deductions to lessen the amount of tax paid per month. Review the last tax return for specific information.

****This category is used for long-term investment planning, such as college education or retirement.

*****This category is added as a guide only. If you have this expense, the percentage shown must be deducted from other budget.

CROWN
Do Well

crown.org

Spending Tracker (A)

Month _____

Year _____

CATEGORY	Income	Tithe/Giving	Taxes	Housing	Food	Transporation	Insurance
Allocated Amount	$	$	$	$	$	$	$
DATE							
1st							
2nd							
3rd							
4th							
5th							
6th							
7th							
8th							
9th							
10th							
11th							
12th							
13th							
14th							
15th							
This Month Subtotal	$	$	$	$	$	$	$
16th							
17th							
18th							
19th							
20th							
21st							
22nd							
23rd							
24th							
25th							
26th							
27th							
28th							
29th							
30th							
31st							
This Month Total	$	$	$	$	$	$	$
This Month Surplus/Deficit	$	$	$	$	$	$	$
Year to Date Spending Plan	$	$	$	$	$	$	$
Year to Date Total	$	$	$	$	$	$	$
Year to Date Surplus/Deficit	$	$	$	$	$	$	$

Plan Summary

This Month		Previous Month/Year to Date		Year to Date	
Total Income	$ _____	Total Income	$ _____	Total Income	$ _____
Minus Total Expenses	$ _____	Minus Total Expenses	$ _____	Minus Total Expenses	$ _____
Equals Surplus/Deficit	$ _____	Equals Surplus/Deficit	$ _____	Equals Surplus/Deficit	$ _____

+ between This Month and Previous Month/Year to Date, **=** between Previous Month/Year to Date and Year to Date

Spending Tracker Ⓑ

CATEGORY	Debts	Entertainment/ Recreation	Clothing	Savings	Medical/ Dental	Miscellaneous	Investments	School/ Child Care
Allocated Amount	$	$	$	$	$	$	$	$
DATE								
1st								
2nd								
3rd								
4th								
5th								
6th								
7th								
8th								
9th								
10th								
11th								
12th								
13th								
14th								
15th								
This Month Subtotal	$	$	$	$	$	$	$	$
16th								
17th								
18th								
19th								
20th								
21st								
22nd								
23rd								
24th								
25th								
26th								
27th								
28th								
29th								
30th								
31st								
This Month Total	$	$	$	$	$	$	$	$
This Month Surplus/Deficit	$	$	$	$	$	$	$	$
Year to Date Spending Plan	$	$	$	$	$	$	$	$
Year to Date Total	$	$	$	$	$	$	$	$
Year to Date Surplus/Deficit	$	$	$	$	$	$	$	$

Estimated Budget

Montly Income

Gross Monthly Income $

Salary	$ _____
Interest	$ _____
Dividends	$ _____
Other Income	$ _____

Less

1. Tithe/Giving	$ _____
2. Taxes (Federal / State / Fica)	$ _____

Net Spendable Income $

- -

Monthly Living Expenses

3. Housing $

Mortgage/Rent	$ _____
Insurance	$ _____
Property taxes	$ _____
Cable TV	$ _____
Electricity	$ _____
Gas	$ _____
Water	$ _____
Sanitation	$ _____
Telephone	$ _____
Maintenance	$ _____
Internet service	$ _____
Other	$ _____

4. Food $

5. Transportation $

Payments	$ _____
Gas & Oil	$ _____
Insurance	$ _____
License/Taxes	$ _____
Maintenance	$ _____
Replacement	$ _____
Other	$ _____

6. Insurance $

Insurance	$ _____
Life	$ _____
Health/Dental	$ _____
Disability	$ _____
Other	$ _____

7. Debts (not including house or auto) $

8. Entertainment/ Recreation $

Eating out	$ _____
Babysitters	$ _____
Activities/Trips	$ _____
Vacation	$ _____
Pets	$ _____
Other	$ _____

9. Clothing $

10. Savings $

11. Medical / Dental $

Doctor	$ _____
Dentist	$ _____
Prescriptions	$ _____
Other	$ _____

12. Miscellaneous $

Toiletries/Cosmetics	$ _____
Beauty/Barber	$ _____
Laundry/Cleaners	$ _____
Allowances	$ _____
Subscriptions	$ _____
Gifts	$ _____
Other	$ _____

13. Investments $

14. School / Childcare $

Tuition	$ _____
Materials	$ _____
Transportation	$ _____
Childcare	$ _____

Total Living Expenses $ [_____]

- -

How the Month Turns Out

NET SPENDABLE INCOME	$ [_____]
– TOTAL LIVING EXPENSES	$ [_____]
	$ [_____]

STAGE FOUR

Teach Your Children

(Presenter: Catherine Brown)

MEMORY VERSE

"Train up a child in the way he should go; even when he is old he will not depart from it."

Proverbs 22:6 (ESV)

LISTENING GUIDE – PART 1

Fill in the blanks as you watch the video.

The term "millennials" designates the group of individuals who are currently 22- to 37-years-old. This group is also known as "_____ ."

Teaching Children Financial Stewardship

Goals:	Reality (now):
God owns _____	I work hard for MY money
Give, save, spend	Spend, borrow, borrow more

Family time

If I can't be with another family

_____

What does this even mean?

Family discussions over a meal

Who eats at the table?

Delayed

When I can have it, NOW?

_____

Purposeful order to everything

Takes too long

Family-determined

Internet/Google/

_____ /

Kardashians

guidelines

How do we teach biblical stewardship when the rules have

_____ ?

STAGE FOUR

Notes

Man's Vision:	God's Vision:
Know Me	Know Him
Find _____	Find _____
Discover a Platform	Discover Purpose
Make a	Make a
_____	_____

If we don't see God's vision, we will settle for a

_____ .

Who Are These Millennials?

Some characteristics:

- Open-minded
- Receptive to new _____
- Upbeat
- Equal rights for minorities
- _____
- Self-expressive
- Liberal
- Accommodating
- Trophy kids

- _____

- Less likely to move forward/"out" from home

- More focused on materialistic values

- Desire a flexible schedule, to be _____

- Want "meaning" behind most everything

- Slowed problem-solving abilities (phone dependent)

As in the example of paying attention to the detour signs vs. following the phone app, we want to ask these young people: "Is what you are doing _____ for you?"

If we are teaching in a way that is not _____ , then we need to think about doing something differently.

Where they are struggling:

- Intense _____ to have "figured out" their plan

- No time to let things "evolve"

- Every action has to "build" the _____

- Want things to be "easy" and do not want to work hard

- _____ is RAMPANT

- Every action must be "_____"

When asked, "What do you see as something that has ballooned in this generation and become overarching?" a licensed therapist replied, "_____ , without question."

Why? They don't have a _____ _____ . They are never away from their phones and the _____ of others.

We've got to figure out a way to guide them forward in their _____ _____ .

Influence of Smart Phones

Millennials get information so quickly that often they don't take the time to _____ where it's coming from—what the genesis is, what the _____ is.

The ability to really focus in and push out _____ is difficult because they are conditioned to react to every single one.

There's a live for the _____ reality: YOLO –

"You Only Live Once."

Desire for _____ is diminished.

As parents or teachers, we feel ill-equipped because we

don't have the _____ , the apps, that can

help us communicate with this group.

What is it that's inside of you that "bubbles up" and you're

so immersed in it that you lose track of time? It takes some

time and effort to find out what you're really designed to do.

An app or likes on your _____ posts are not

going to help you figure that out.

Pastor Chris Hodges, when faced with statistics showing

that more members of his church were attending their small

groups than attending the church services, said:

"We must be _____ in our modern reality...

regardless of how we _____ about it."

As parents and teachers, we've got to shift our thinking from "They just don't get it" to "How can I form my language, build a model, build a slide deck that will bring these younger people into the reality of what we're dealing with in _____ _____ ?"

We've got to figure out a way to be relevant in our _____ .

LISTENING GUIDE – PART 2

Fill in the blanks as you watch the video.

Instead of a spreadsheet, millennials would prefer an _____ on their phone.

The reworked guideline budget visually helps them see if they are out of alignment with what is _____ . *(See sample on page 67.)*

Example: Suzie Spender – The team populated an income statement based on realistic, but fictitious, spending habits.

The point of this example: If you don't know where you are, then you will absolutely fall into the trap of getting to the end of the month and _____ .

Exercise: Balance Suzie's Budget – The millennials were asked to take the statement home and balance Suzie's budget. They returned with this comment: "_____ _____ ." (*See sample on page 68.*)

Example: True Cost of Debt – When tempted to make a major purchase "now," first do the math. See how much more you are going to pay if you buy that item on _____ .

We have to help them do this in a _____ way.

Example: Value of Growth Over Time (compounding interest). Bottom line:
Any opportunity you have to _____
what you are saving early on, don't touch it—let it
_____ , and it will be a sizable amount when
you get to the age when you're ready to stop working.

Exercise: Buy Groceries – Students were asked to conduct a price check on several items from different stores, from high end to low end. Bottom line: There is a great difference in cost based on the store. If the least expensive grocery item were purchased from each category vs. the most expensive, they would save $ _____ .

We've got to get them the info they need to " _____ _____ " and move into the rest of their lives and not be encumbered by _____ .

Learning Tool: Millennials were given a set of cards with Scripture memory verses that were paired with a practical _____ .

Tips for Parents with Teens

Here are some great suggestions from Rob Hays-St Claire of JH Ranch in California.

Ingredient #1: Create a regular sabbatical _____ from technology.

Ingredient #2: Teach and model character in addition to

setting _____ .

Ingredient #3: Create regular and memorable moments that

don't involve _____ .

Ingredient #4: Become our children's _____

_____ of affirmation and encouragement.

Parents need to invest the time to _____

with them to help them understand God's perfect order in all

of this.

Ingredient #5: Find a family with children a little older

than yours that share your same family values and

_____ _____ !

DISCUSSION QUESTIONS

Be prepared to discuss your responses within your group.

1. Read 1 Corinthians 9:19-23. How does this ministry principle apply to teaching millennials (and teens) the message of biblical stewardship?

2. If you are a millennial, or if you are a parent or friend of millennials, would you agree that anxiety is a big issue with this segment of the population?

   Why or why not?

What (or where) do you consider to be your "safe place"?

3. In a couple of sentences, name two or three practical steps the church can take to become more relevant to younger generations.

4. Thinking back to the Suzie Spender example, do you see some of your own spending tendencies in Suzie Spender's income statement? Name one or two.

5. People sometimes describe the example of compounding interest as both motivating and discouraging. Which is it for you? Why do you think that is?

6. Proverbs 1:8 says, *"Hear, my son, your father's instruction, and forsake not your mother's teaching"* (ESV). Why is it important for parents to be their children's primary source of affirmation and encouragement?

NEXT STEPS AND GOALS

As you reflect on the video and discussion questions from Stage Four, who are the children, grandchildren, friends, neighbors, relatives, or children and youth in your church and community who God may be calling you to influence? What are the next steps He is asking you to take to teach His biblical principles to the next generation?

Raising Money Wise Kids: Lessons and Activities for 8-12 year olds and *Essentials for Raising Money-Wise Teens* are two Crown resources available to help you teach the children and youth in your life God's principles for finances.

FORMS/WORKSHEETS

For your reference, on the following pages we've included two of the worksheets Catherine shared during her session:

1. **Estimated Budget Calculator**

2. **Spending Plan Example**

CROWN
Do Well

Estimated Budget Calculator

STEP ONE: Input Salary
STEP TWO: View Suggested Budget
STEP THREE: Input Actual Expenses

① INPUT SALARY

Expected/Average Monthly Income

SOURCE	AMOUNT
Income Source 1	
Income Source 2	
Other	
Gross Income	**$0**

LESS	
Tithing (10%)	$0
Taxes (25%)	$0
Net Spendable Income	**$0**

② VIEW SUGGESTED BUDGET

Monthly Expenses (Suggested Range)

Item	Range		Min	Max
Rent/Mortgage	28% -	40%	$ -	$ -
Food	10% -	16%	$ -	$ -
Transportation	12% -	16%	$ -	$ -
Insurance	4% -	6%	$ -	$ -
Debt	0% -	6%	$ -	$ -
Entertainment/Recreation	2% -	8%	$ -	$ -
Clothing	4% -	8%	$ -	$ -
Savings	4% -	10%	$ -	$ -
Medical	4% -	8%	$ -	$ -
Miscellaneous	4% -	8%	$ -	$ -
Investments	0% -	8%	$ -	$ -
Other				
Other				
Total			**$ -**	**$ -**

③

	Actual Amount	Actual %
		#DIV/0!
		#DIV/0!
		#DIV/0!
		#DIV/0!
		#DIV/0!
		#DIV/0!
		#DIV/0!
		#DIV/0!
		#DIV/0!
		#DIV/0!
		#DIV/0!
		#DIV/0!
		#DIV/0!
	$	

■ Income ■ Expenses

$1
$1
$1
$1
$1
$1
$0
$0
$0
$0

Summary

TOTAL MONTHLY INCOME
$0

TOTAL MONTHLY EXPENSES
$0

MONTHLY SAVINGS
$0

CASH BALANCE
$0

Rent/Mortgage
Food
Transportation
Insurance
Entertainment/Recreation
Clothing
Savings
Medical
Miscellaneous

CROWN
Do Well

DIRECTIONS: Fill in true amounts by all blue sub-categories. The white cells will fill in automatically. When you are finished, view your spending surplus or deficit below.

MONTHLY TOTALS

Net Spendable Income	$ 2,600.00
Monthly Living Expenses	$ 3,075.00
Surplus or Deficit	$ (475.00)

MONTHLY INCOME

Gross Monthly Income	$ 4,000.00
Salary	
Interest	
Dividends	
Other Income	
Less	
1. Tithe/Giving	$ 400.00
2. Taxes	$ 1,000.00
3. Pre Tax Investments	

NET SPENDABLE INCOME

	$ 2,600.00

MONTHLY LIVING EXPENSES

4. Housing		9. Entertainment/Rec.	
Mortgage/Rent	$ 870.00	Eating Out	$ 550.00
Insurance	600.00	Babysitters	200.00
Property Taxes		Activities/Trips	200.00
Cable TV	50.00	Vacation	
Electricity	40.00	Pets	150.00
Gas		Other	150.00
Water		10. Clothing	
Sanitation		Clothing	-
Telephone	80.00	11. Savings	
Maintenance		Savings (Short Term)	45.00
Internet Service	100.00	12. Medical	
Other		Doctor	
5. Food (Groceries)		Dentist	
Groceries	200.00	Prescriptions	510.00
6. Transportation		Other	
Payments	575.00	13. Miscellaneous	
Gas & Oil	300.00	Toiletries/Cosmetics	45.00
Insurance	175.00	Beauty/Barber	150.00
License/Taxes	100.00	Laundry/Cleaners	25.00
Maint./Repair/Replace		Allowances	
7. Insurance		Subscriptions (Blue Apron)	95.00
Health	175.00	Gifts	75.00
Dental	75.00	Cash	100.00
Disability	100.00	Other (Spotify)	10.00
Life		Other (Hulu)	10.00
8. Debts		14. Investments	
Credit Card(s)	-	Investments (Long Term)	-
Loans		15. Childcare/Senior Care	
Other (____)		Tuition	-
Other (____)		Materials/Supplies	
		Transportation	
		Day Care/Senior Living Expenses	

TOTAL LIVING EXPENSES

	$ 3,075.00

STAGE FIVE

Finish Well

Finish Well

(Presenter: David McAlvany)

"Most of what God gives you in life . . . is not for you."

—Larry Burkett

MEMORY VERSE

His master replied, "Well done, good and faithful servant! You have been faithful with a few things; I will put you in charge of many things. Come and share your master's happiness!"

Matthew 25:21 (NIV)

Note: Before watching this session, you may want to watch the following video clip which David references at the beginning of his message: http://bit.ly/TotalLifeStewardship5

LISTENING GUIDE – PART 1

Fill in the blanks as you watch the video.

"Finishing well" may boil down to this: All that you

_____ , all that you _____ and all

that you _____ is not just for you.

Stewardship is all encompassing. We are stewards of our:

Family life

It includes relationships, intimacy and the requirement

of forgiveness and grace (set on a foundation of

_____ to others)

Culture

It's defined as our values and hopes as we express them

in our daily lives in the _____ that we make

each day.

Heritage

This includes where we have come from as a distinct

_____ _____ and as a group.

Ideas

Ideas such as _____ , love and grace

define us as they find a living _____ in our

lives. They are the things that we live for, the things that we

die for.

Intangibles

These include feelings and _____ .

STAGE FIVE

Notes

Physical Health

Process of Growth and Maturity

It reflects our Creator's design and shows up as one part

_____ _____ from us, two

parts grace and mercy from God.

Wealth

"Finishing well" can be defined as stewarding to our very last

breath all God's resources toward the _____

He designed and intended.

Everyone cares about legacy, and most everyone recognizes

that finishing well is not the _____ in your

checkbook. Finishing well involves the proper management

of tangible and _____ resources.

It's the management of intangibles that truly defines

_____ and success.

The intangibles include: cultivating love, cultivating

_____ , learning to extend grace to each

other, practicing _____ . The intangibles

really hold families together through thick and thin.

Legacy is not simply what we leave at the end of our lives,

but it's the _____ _____ of our

values and choices that we make throughout life.

Success and finishing well are _____ .

Example of Not Finishing Well

King Saul

He is defined by his end: bitterness, anger, loss of

_____ , tragedy.

If we look at our own lives, we will find that in some

categories we have done well and are on track to finishing

well. In other categories we may not currently be on the

right _____ .

Saul had his strengths and he also had his

_____ . As he neared the end of his life,

those weaknesses became more pronounced and they

remained _____ . Those weaknesses

defined how he finished.

Examples of Finishing Well

King David

A life of mistakes did not rob a man of _____

to finish well.

David's life was a mess, and his family life was far from

_____ . But God still used him, and still used

the family.

David McAlvany's family mantra from the life of David:

What do you do when you fall down? You _____

_____ _____ again.

Paul

Paul is perhaps the clearest example in Scripture of what it

means to finish well. Not everything he did was successful

(_____ , for example). Not everyone with the

opportunity to finish well _____ to.

LISTENING GUIDE – PART 2

Fill in the blanks as you watch the video.

Six Steps to Finishing Well

1. **Get Perspective.**

Can you remove yourself from the _____

_____ perspective and shift your perspective

to the third person? Can you see yourself from the

observer's point of view? Can you see your life objectively?

2. **Take Inventory of the Little Things.**

Fishes and Loaves fed five thousand. What are you working

with? Sometimes we lack the _____ for

what God can do with what we give Him.

God is more interested in your story, your

_____ , than He is interested or in need of

your checkbook.

3. **Take Inventory of the Good and the Bad Things.**

Account for the assets at your disposal and

_____ you carry.

Notes

God has a _____ thread woven throughout our lives, from beginning to end. We get to see our liabilities changed in the equation to assets.

4. Reflect on the Voice You Have and the Voice You've Lost.

Identify areas in which you have been _____ and remember that all Satan means for evil God can turn to good. Nurture a redemptive ethic.

The redemptive ethic says, what was lost can be found. Yes, you do have an accuser, but you also have a

_____ .

God's voice of authority returns to us through humility, _____ , confession, forgiveness.

Speaking life and hope into the lives of others frequently comes from those areas where we personally have experienced _____ and have subsequently seen redemption and new life in Christ Jesus.

5. Recognize Your Unique Ministry.

Only in God's economy can liabilities on your life balance

sheet be flipped to _____ .

Your ministry is tied to your story. This is your

_____ capstone.

6. Take Action.

Everything in your life has been preparation for the final

stretch. Paul said to Timothy: I charge you with this, fulfill

your _____ .

Commenting on his father's work in the Philippines, David

McAlvany said, "His _____ is now his

ministry. That is redemption."

Bring all that you are and all that you have into the light of

God's _____, and figure out—before it's too

late—who it's for. Most is not for you.

DISCUSSION QUESTIONS

Be prepared to discuss your responses within your group.

1. In light of the truth that most of what God gives us in life is not for us, evaluate your own efforts in stewarding such things as family, ideas and your spiritual growth. Are you intentional? How can you improve?

2. What are some practical steps you can take now to set a trajectory to finish well in these non-financial areas?

3. In 1 Chronicles 10:14, we read that King Saul *"died for his breach of faith. He broke faith with the Lord..."* (ESV). How can taking inventory of your strengths and weaknesses help you avoid a legacy of regret?

4. Although King David was far from perfect, God describes him as *"a man after my heart"* (Acts 13:22). Describe someone you know who, after he or she had fallen, got up again and finished well.

5. Our enemy, Satan, tries to neutralize our "voice" through the shame of our failures. Name some character qualities that open the way for God's voice of authority and life to be restored to us through His redeeming work.

6. Are you willing, by God's grace, to allow your "redeemed failures" to become your ministry?

7. Name some ways others can be helped through this part of your legacy.

NEXT STEPS AND GOALS

As you reflect on the video and discussion questions from Stage Five, how is God leading you to be more intentional with your non-financial legacy (family, ideas, spiritual growth, redeemed failures)? What steps is He asking you to take today in order to finish well?

For more on how to Finish Well, check out David McAlvany's book, *The Intentional Legacy: What You Want for Your Family, Why You Want It, and How You Get There* at http://bit.ly/IntentionalLegacy.

STAGE FIVE

FORMS/WORKSHEETS

"All that you are, all that you know and all that you have is not just for you."
—David McAlvany

As you prayerfully consider your legacy, there may be people, things, ideas, successes, failures or other resources that God is asking you to surrender to Him. Use the **Transfer of Ownership** worksheet on the following page to declare to God that:

1. You understand all of these things belong to Him.

2. He has entrusted them to you as His steward.

3. You desire to use all He has given you to advance His Kingdom for His glory.

TRANSFER OF OWNERSHIP

Made the _____ day of _____

From: _____

To: The Lord

I (we) hereby transfer to the Lord the ownership of the
following possessions:

_____   _____

_____   _____

_____   _____

_____   _____

_____   _____

Witnesses who hold me (us)
accountable in the recognition of
the Lord's ownership: Stewards of the possessions above:

_____   _____

_____   _____

This instrument is not a binding legal document and cannot be used to transfer property.

ANSWER KEY

Stage One
Part 1
hope
purpose
destiny
identity
purpose
bitter
chocolate
brewed
obligations
retirement
potential
satisfaction
80
understand
life

Stage One
Part 2
1
individual
inside
outside
womb
sanctified
ordained
Character
change
permanent
environment
personality
energy
natural
thinking
align
perfect
passion
purpose
purpose
truth

Stage Two
Part 1
Recession
paradigm
water
relationship
Scripture
success
earthquake
fuel
Augmented
DNA
bubble
education
relevant
automation
empathy
radiologists
2 trillion
transportation
driverless
e-commerce
failure
design
6 years

Stage Two
Part 2
Learn
failure
correction
stop
environment
gifts
leverage
lazy
ethic
grow
direction
glory of God
faith
back

Stage Three
Part 1
45
78
epidemic
advice
God's Word
ignorant
principles
money
stewardship
you
give
pray
fast
real
money
value
Kingdom
indicator
throne
security
upside down
provider
stewardship

Stage Three
Part 2
firstfruits
God
treasures
nothing
Great Commission
steward
savings
savings rate
tragedy
97
provider
treasures
save
Kingdom
thingdom
belongs
heart

Stage Four
Part 1
Gen Y
everything
Contentment
gratification
morals
changed
Fame
Dime
Freedom
Difference
counterfeit
ideas
Confident
Coddled
accommodated
working
resonating
pressure
resume
Anxiety
impressive
Anxiety
safe place
scrutiny
current reality
filter
root
distractions
moment
conversation
language
Facebook
relevant
feel
biblical stewardship
reality

Stage Four
Part 2
app
expected
overspending
It's hard
credit
methodical
maximize
grow
15.38
adult well
debt
application
rhythm
limits
technology
primary source
connect
ask questions

Stage Five
Part 1
are
know
have
commitment
choices
family unit
justice
expression
sentimentality
purposeful action
purposes
balance
intangible
legacy
loyalty
kindness
sum total
values
multifaceted
faith
trajectory
weaknesses
untransformed
vision
perfect
get back up
Demas
chooses

Stage Five
Part 2
first person
imagination
testimony
liabilities
redemptive
neutralized
Redeemer
transparency
death
assets
legacy
ministry
wound
grace
not

KNOW YOUR DESIGN

Look inside your heart and mind with Personality I.D.

Personality I.D. is a proven and powerful DISC diagnostic tool that looks inside your psyche to give you a better understanding of what motivates you and how you interact with others. This unfiltered view gives you the opportunity to maximize your potential, be more productive, and better understand your relationships with others.

Personality I.D.®

Through Personality I.D. you will:

- Understand your God-given personality
- Gain confidence in your interactions with others
- Address personal weaknesses constructively
- Acquire valuable insight for conflict resolution

Take your first step to discovering who God created you to be.

Visit: www.crown.org/pid

Approach Your Work — and Life — from a Biblical Perspective!

How has God designed you? And how can you best steward this design to bring Him glory and experience the joy of fulfillment and satisfaction in your work and life?

You don't have to wonder anymore!

Whether you're a student preparing for the future, a mid-career adult looking for a change, or a retiree trying to figure out what comes next, Crown's proven *Career Direct* assessment can help you utilize your design for maximum impact.

What makes *Career Direct* unique?

● Focuses on four key dimensions: Personality, Interests, Skills, and Values

● Produces a detailed 34-page report that clearly lays out your work profile

● Includes additional resources to assist you in researching educational and career fields that might be a fit for you.

● One of our trained *Career Direct* Consultants will meet with you to go over your results and help think through your next steps toward fulfilling God's purpose.

PERSONALITY

VALUES

INTERESTS

SKILLS

Career Direct®
LIVING *by Design*™

Overcoming Financial Challenges To Help You Achieve a Life of Meaning and Purpose

Don't wait to begin your journey!
crown.org/mlpfs